Ex-clue-sive Screening

T5-AFD-814

You settle into your first-class seat on your flight to Stockholm. To prepare for the adventure, you check out your English-to-Swedish dictionary. The Swedish alphabet has three extra letters that are written Ä, Å, and Ö.

After studying for a while, you decide to take a break and watch the plane's movie. You switch on your video screen. Instead of a movie, there's an important clue from Top Secret Headquarters! The three extra Swedish letters will help you tell which letters to choose to decode the message below.

CODE

When you see **Å**, use the letter after it.

When you see **Ä**, write the letter before it.

When you see **Ö**, start a new word.

ÅOÅUÅRÖÅaGÄEÄÅNÅTÖÅONÄÖTÄÅOÅPÖOÄÅFÖMÄ
ÅOÅUÅNTÄÖÅKEÄBÄÅNEÄÅKAÄIÄÅSÅEÖFÄÅOÅU
NÄÅDÖNÄÅOÅTHÄÄIÅNÅGÖBÄÅUÅTÖÅBÅEAÄÅU
ÅTIÄFÄÅULÄÖVÄÅIEÄÅWÅS

The first word of this message is OUR.

TOP SECRET TIP

Have you decoded the message? Use it to cross one place off your list on page 30.

HIDDEN CROOKS

You arrive in Stockholm on a beautiful sunny day. After checking into your hotel, you decide to explore Sweden's capital. You start in a section of the city called Old Town, or *Gamla Stan*. After a stroll through the narrow cobblestone streets, you feel as if you have returned to medieval times. Soon you find yourself in Stortorget, an open town square. Good news, Top Secret Agent! Your square route has led you right to your next clue!

Five of the suspects are circling the square with you. The sixth was caught chasing the pigeons and was led squarely away by the local *polis*. Search the scene to find the five suspects. You can get this clue all squared away by circling each one you find.

Use your villain cards to help you find the crooks. They are wearing the same clothes as on the cards.

TOP SECRET TIP

Did you find all five crooks? Good work! Now turn to page 28 and cross off the suspect you did *not* find. He or she could not have committed the crime. The other five are still suspects.

What's on Sail?

You trail a shady character through the narrow, twisting streets of Old Town and into central Stockholm. But when you reach the water's edge near City Hall, the sneaky suspect is nowhere to be seen on land. You rent a sailboat to search the water.

From your boat, the view of City Hall, or *Stadshuset,* is simply spectacular. While enjoying the sights, you also keep a watch out for your next clue. There's something bobbing in the water toward your boat. It's a bottle with a message in it that was sent by another agent!

To crack the code, look at the Swedish number word under the first line of the message on page 5. Use the key to figure out what number it is. Then look for the sail with that number, and write its letter on the line. Continue like this until you've filled in the message.

You will need to use both the KEY and your guidebook.

TOP SECRET TIP

MESSAGE

___ ___ ___   ___ ___ ___ ___   ___ ___ ___ ___ ___
tre tio fem   tre nittio tolv fyrtio   fyra tolv fem ett nittio

___ ___ ___ ___:
elva fyrtio nio tio

___ ___ ___   ___ ___ ___ ___   ___ ___ ___ ___   ___ ___
fem ett tio   elva två sju tio   fyra två åtta sju   tolv tre

" ___ ___ ___ ___ ".
  tjugo fyrtio nio tio

KEY

11 = elva	20 = tjugo
12 = tolv	40 = fyrtio
90 = nittio	

Other numbers you need are in your guidebook. **P 31**

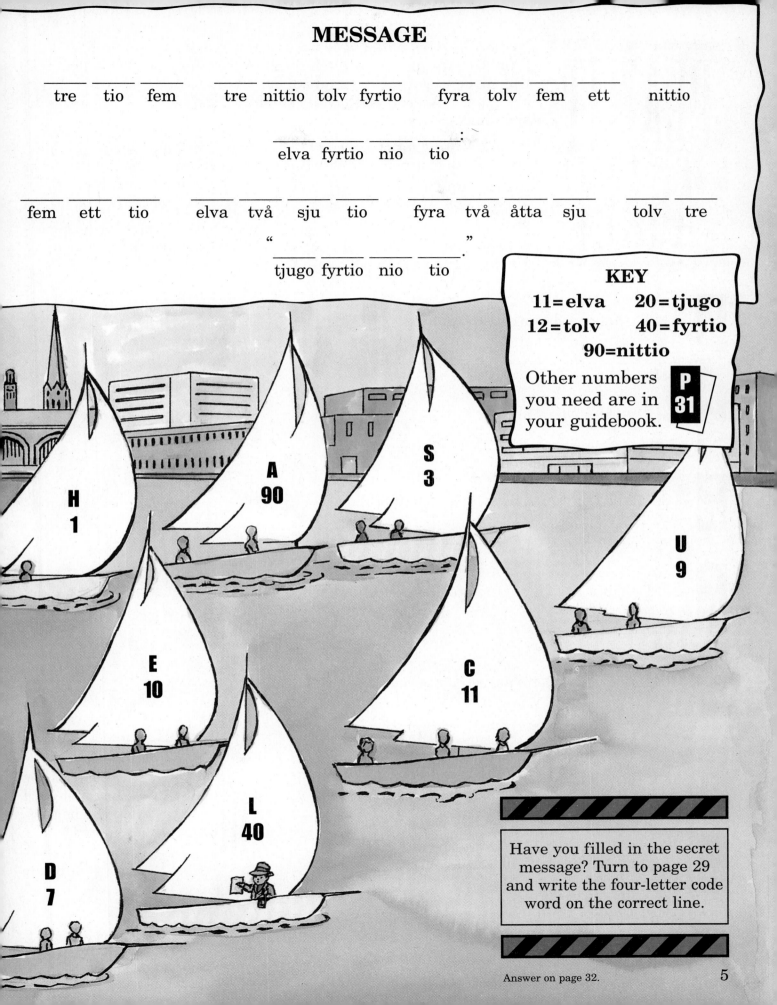

H 1
A 90
S 3
U 9
E 10
C 11
L 40
D 7

Have you filled in the secret message? Turn to page 29 and write the four-letter code word on the correct line.

PLAY IT AGAIN

You let the wind out of your sails and walk back to *Gamla Stan*. From Old Town, it's just a ten-minute ferryboat ride to the island of Djurgården. Stockholm is spread over many islands, and this one is a popular gathering spot in the summer. Many festivals, concerts, and dances are held here.

While scouting for clues, you notice posters for an outdoor play. You act on your instincts and decide to attend. As you settle into your seat, a mysterious-looking usher hands you a program filled with information. It looks as if it is time to perform, Top Secret Agent!

Fill in the answers on this page. Then write the letters in the spaces with the same numbers on page 7. When you've got the message, direct yourself to the bottom of the page.

P 26 1. The largest national park in Sweden

__ __ __ __ __ __ __ __ __ __
1   2   3

P 4 2. Sweden's biggest river

__ __ __ __ __ __ __
   4   5

P 20 3. Method by which Sweden gets half of its power

__ __ __ __ __ __ __ __ __ __ __ __ __ __ __
6   7   8

P 16 4. Province known as "the breadbasket of Sweden"

__ __ __ __ __
9   10

P 11 5. Name of Sweden's annual cross-country race

__ __ __ __ __ __ __ __ __ __ __ __
  11   12

P 4 6. First woman to win the Nobel Prize in literature

__ __ __ __ __ __ __ __ __ __ __
    13   14   15

P 12 7. Home of Sweden's oldest university

__ __ __ __ __ __
16   17

> You will need your Top Secret Guidebook for this puzzle. Look for each answer on the page that is listed.

> TOP SECRET TIP

$\overline{6}$ $\overline{12}$ $\overline{1}$ $\overline{10}$ $\overline{8}$ $\overline{12}$ $\overline{16}$ $\overline{7}$ $\overline{10}$ $\overline{3}$ $\overline{12}$ $\overline{4}$ $\overline{6}$ $\overline{16}$ $\overline{3}$ $\overline{14}$ $\overline{7}$ $\overline{8}$ $\overline{4}$ $\overline{6}$ $\overline{10}$

$\overline{9}$ $\overline{4}$ $\overline{12}$ $\overline{17}$ $\overline{10}$ $\overline{3}$ $\overline{11}$ $\overline{4}$ $\overline{10}$ $\overline{13}$ $\overline{11}$ $\overline{9}$ $\overline{3}$ $\overline{12}$ $\overline{4}$

$\overline{3}$ $\overline{10}$ $\overline{5}$ $\overline{7}$ $\overline{15}$ $\overline{12}$ $\overline{12}$ $\overline{2}$.

When you've filled in the spaces, use the clue to cross another location off the list on page 30.

Answer on page 32.

Rocking Runes

The Göta Canal connects Stockholm with Göteborg, Sweden's second-largest city. A relaxing canal boat ride will give you time to do some important reading about this case, so you hop aboard and open a book about Swedish rune stones.

Rune stones are rocks with ancient carvings on them. Many rune stones were carved by Swedish Vikings. The carvings tell about Vikings and give accounts of their activities many hundreds of years ago. More rune stones have been found in Sweden than in any other country.

The boat rocks as you hit a wave. You drop the book, and out slips a piece of paper. You realize it's "Göta" be a clue! Rock-solid thinking, Top Secret Agent! Although the paper contains a drawing that looks like an ancient rune stone, it is actually a maze. Find a path from start to finish. Then check the bottom of page 9 and put this rune in tune.

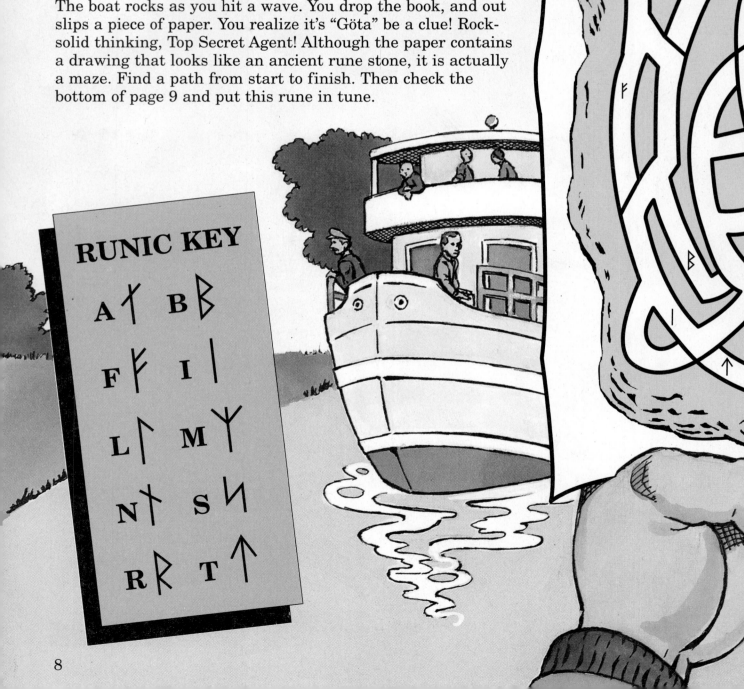

RUNIC KEY

8

CONTENTS

WHO

WHO DID IT?

WHAT

WHAT WAS STOLEN?

WHERE

WHERE IS IT HIDDEN?

TOP SECRET TIPS

Look for tips on the different pages of your puzzle book. They will help you solve many of the puzzles.

VILLAIN CARDS

These cards provide clues about six sneaky suspects.

TOP SECRET GUIDEBOOK

Your guidebook contains information you need to crack the case. When you see this symbol, look up the fact in your guidebook.

FINISH

Have you found the correct path? There are
seven runic letters on the way. Translate
the letters to complete this message:

__ __ __ __ __ __ " __ __ __ ."

Now turn to page 29 and write the three-letter
code word on the correct line.

Fish Stories

After a long boat ride, you arrive in Göteborg and go directly to your hotel. There is a message from Top Secret Headquarters waiting at the front desk. According to HQ, some fishermen in a nearby village have spotted the crook! You must head there immediately. You hire a taxicab to take you up the coast to the village.

Sweden is a fisherman's paradise. For hundreds of years, people have been making a living fishing off Sweden's western coast.

You soon find the folks who caught a glimpse of your crook. They're all willing to talk about what they saw. Something's fishy here, though. Only one of your witnesses got a "reel" good look at the suspect. To find the true witness, read the five clues on page 11. Then land your answer.

No, no! There was no pooch with the thief.

I saw stars on the thief's shirt.

The crook you are looking for had a dog.

Read the clues in the box on page 11. Then cross off each fisherman until there is only one left. That person has the true clue.

TOP SECRET TIP

"Smör" Clues

Back in Göteborg, you stroll down Kungsportsavenyn. This famous street, known as the *Avenyn*, is filled with sightseers, shops, and cafés. Your stomach rumbles, giving you a clue that you need to eat! You duck into a restaurant and head for the long smörgåsbord table. The table is loaded with many delicious things to eat. You pile your plate high with herring, salmon, Swedish meatballs, salads, cheeses, and Swedish pancakes. Take it easy, Top Secret Agent! You can always come back for seconds!

You head to your seat and unfold your napkin. Someone's left you a message! It looks as if you have some more choices to make. Answer these questions about Sweden to cook up a tasty new clue.

You will need your Top Secret Guidebook to solve this puzzle. The page numbers show you where to look for each answer.

P ??

TOP SECRET TIP

P 18

1. Off the west coast of southern Sweden is a stretch of sea called the Kattegat. What does *Kattegat* mean?

   c. cat's whiskers   **n. cat's mouth**
   s. cat's throat

P 4

2. What is Swedish money called?

   a. sverige   **n. krona**
   o. malmö

3. What is the name of Sweden's oldest amusement park?

> **d. Sju Flags over Skåne**
> **e. Folkets Park**
> **f. Malmö Amusements**

6. Which of these Hollywood stars was *not* from Sweden?

> **a. Audrey Hepburn**
> **e. Ingrid Bergman   o. Greta Garbo**

4. Which of these musical groups is *not* from Sweden?

> **a. ABBA   d. The Cranberries**
> **l. The Cardigans**

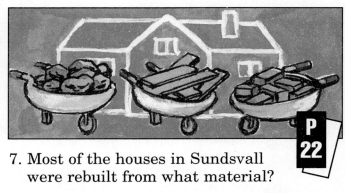

7. Most of the houses in Sundsvall were rebuilt from what material?

> **g. stone   i. wood   t. brick**

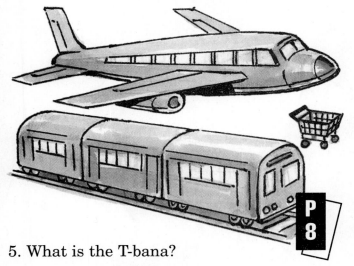

5. What is the T-bana?

> **h. Stockholm's airport**
> **n. Stockholm's largest shopping center**
> **r. Stockholm's subway system**

Did you circle the letter of each correct answer? Now write the circled letters, in order from *last* to *first*, in the spaces below to complete a clue.

The stolen item is not in the

____ ____ ____ ____ ____ ____ ____.

Turn to page 30 and use this clue to cross one location off the list.

Head of the Glass

On a tip from another agent, you head southeast to the area of Sweden known as *Glasriket,* or the Kingdom of Crystal. Sweden is famous for its glassware and crystal. You go to the town of Kosta, where the oldest Swedish glassworks was founded in 1742. According to your source, a suspect was spotted here breaking a glass and not paying for it.

You go from shop to shop interviewing the shop owners and glassblowers. The trail is getting as cold as a glass full of ice in Lapland. Then you step into one shop and notice a unique pattern in the display of glassware. Suddenly, things are crystal clear. Use the glass pieces on display to fill in the message on page 15. Then check the bottom of that page.

Your villain cards will help with this clue.

TOP SECRET TIP

MESSAGE

Have you cracked the glass code? Great work, Top Secret Agent! Now turn to page 28 and use this information to cross one suspect off your list.

Answer on page 32.

cast of castles

The trail leads you to the nearby town of Kalmar. This coastal town is the home of Kalmar Castle. Southern Sweden has more than 200 beautiful old castles and manor houses. You've read that parts of Kalmar Castle date back to the twelfth century, but you're hoping to turn up a more recent development inside.

You buy a ticket to tour the castle. While standing outside waiting for your tour to begin, you realize that Kalmar is not the only castle the ticket is good for. Your ticket is covered with Swedish castle names. You get the re-"moat" idea that it's a clue. No wonder Top Secret Headquarters chose you for this assignment!

Circle each of the castle names in the grid on page 17. After you find them all, check out the bottom of the page.

The castle names are hidden across, up, down, and diagonally. Some of them are written backward.

TOP SECRET TIP

SWEDEN CASTLES

BÄCKASKOG
ENGSÖ
GÅSEVADHOLM
GÄVLE
HALMSTAD
HÄSSELBY
KALMAR
LÄCKÖ
MALMÖHUS
SJÖÖ
SKOKLOSTER
SKOTTORP
SOFIERO
STJERNSUND
STRÖMSHOLM
TIDÖ
TJOLÖHOLM
TORUP
UPPSALA
VADSTENA

D	R	E	T	S	O	L	K	O	K	S	W
R	N	I	S	U	H	Ö	M	L	A	M	M
T	L	U	E	U	P	P	S	A	L	A	L
H	Ä	S	S	E	L	B	Y	O	M	N	O
H	C	P	T	N	H	I	H	P	A	E	H
A	K	U	S	G	R	S	Ö	R	R	T	D
L	Ö	R	O	S	M	E	Ö	O	N	S	A
M	L	O	H	Ö	L	O	J	T	T	D	V
S	H	T	R	E	D	L	S	T	I	A	E
T	N	T	O	R	E	I	F	O	S	V	S
A	S	E	L	V	Ä	G	T	K	E	R	Å
D	E	D	B	Ä	C	K	A	S	K	O	G

Did you circle all the words? Now write the leftover letters in the spaces below to spell out a colorful clue. Be sure to go in order from left to right and top to bottom.

___ ___ ___ ___ ___   ___ ___ ___ ___ ___   ___ ___   ___ ___ ___

___ ___ ___ ___: " ___ ___ ___ ."

Turn to page 29, and write your clue in the correct place.

WALLED IN

You follow a lead and head north to Oskarshamn. From there, you ride a ferry to the island of Gotland. Ringed with white sandy beaches, this large island is a vacation paradise for Swedes. You can't take time to enjoy the sand and surf, Top Secret Agent, there's a case to be solved!

You rent a bicycle and start touring the island. The trail takes you to Visby. This town, which dates from the Middle Ages, is famous for the seventeenth-century wall that surrounds it. As you pause to admire one of the forty-four towers in the limestone wall, you think perhaps you may have been pedaling in the hot sun too long. You're starting to see pictures in the wall! Find the six hidden objects to "wall-tz" away with your next clue.

Use the picture clues on page 19 to help you find the hidden objects.

TOP SECRET TIP

Östersund

Öland

Archipelago

Falun

Kebnekaise

Stockholm

Have you found all the hidden items?
One of them is hidden twice. Find that
one and use the clue word under its picture
to cross off a location on page 30.

DANCING DAYS

While you are on Gotland, an urgent message comes over your Top Secret beeper. You must fly to the province of Dalarna to attend a Midsummer's Eve Festival. This festival takes place throughout Sweden each year near the end of June. To celebrate the return of summer, many Swedes stay up most of the night. They perform traditional folk dances around maypoles and eat Swedish delicacies.

You arrive in Dalarna in time to join in a Maypole dance. Nice footwork, Top Secret Agent! The kids dancing with you are dressed in their traditional local costumes. Each has a fact to tell. You have a Top Secret feeling that some of the statements may not be true. Use your guidebook to see who has their facts straight.

Use your Top Secret Guidebook to check the facts in this puzzle. The page numbers show you where to look for each answer.

TOP SECRET TIP

P12 Have you been to Gränna? It is famous for its striped candy.

P7 In Sweden, our king and queen have complete control of the government.

P6 Sweden is about twice the size of California.

P20 Most Swedes prefer downhill racing to cross-country skiing.

You call our country Sweden, but we call it Sverige.

P 31

P 12

Have you been to the Domkyrkan in Linköping? Beneath its spire are 800-year-old skeletons!

In Swedish, we don't capitalize the names of months or days of the week.

P 31

P 26

Every fall in the town of Jukkasjärvi, a hotel is made from ice!

Count the number of statements that are false. Use that number to find the correct clue below.

Two false?
Cross off the suspect who took forget-me-nots.

Three false?
Cross off the one who took ripe bananas.

Four false?
Cross off the one who took lemons and limes.

Now turn to page 28 and use the clue's instructions and your villain cards to cross off one suspect.

Answer on page 33.

Horsing Around

Your horse sense tells you to explore more of Dalarna. This province is known as the folklore district of Sweden. Old folk traditions remain an important part of everyday life here.

You head to the small village of Nusnäs. You think you see the shadow of a suspect in a shop window there. You step inside the shop, but find only the shopkeeper and a display of Dalecarlian horses. These horses are one of the traditional folk crafts from Dalarna.

You decide to buy one of these hand-painted toy horses as a Top Secret souvenir. As you search the display of horses, you discover that there are two horses that are perfect for you. To ride away with another clue, find the two horses that match exactly.

Did you find the matching horses?
Good job! Each of the two horses is standing
on a different color. Write these two colors,
in order from left to right, here:

_____ and _____

Now write these colors on
the lines on page 29.

Answer on page 33.

Reindeer Games

You take a train north into the vast wilderness of Sweden's Norrland region. You visit small town after small town, tracking your suspect. The temperature may be dropping as you travel north, but the trail is heating up!

At Jokkmokk, just north of the Arctic Circle, you head west to Lapland's Padjelanta National Park. You strap on your backpack and hike into Europe's largest national park. You climb higher and higher, hot on the trail. Suddenly, you round a curve and the trail is lost! It's been trampled by a herd of reindeer!

Don't worry, all is not lost, Top Secret Agent. Count the number of hoofprints in the scene. Then hoof it to the box on page 25 to "rein" in another clue.

It might be helpful to number each hoofprint as you count it.

TOP SECRET TIP

Find the correct number below.
It has a clue phrase next to it.

91 hoofprints? Normal pardons
93 hoofprints? Whopper pine
95 hoofprints? Grinned Jill

The clue phrase rhymes with the name
of one of the locations on page 30.
Cross this place off your list.

Sunny, Sunny Night

In the northern reaches of Sweden, the summer sun shines nearly 24 hours each day. You won't need nearly that long to wrap up this case—you're so close to finishing! But before you leave Sweden, you do have one more clue to light upon.

You hurry east to Överkalix. You've received a hot tip that the local mountain named Brannaberget is one of the best spots to view the famous midnight sun. As you admire the view from the mountain, you realize there's something spotty about this sun. You slip on your Top Secret shades for a better look. You can see clearly now—the last clue is in focus!

Shed light on your final Sweden clue by filling in the grid on page 27. The answers link together—the last letter of one answer becomes the first letter of the next answer. When you're done, beam to the bottom of the page.

Your guidebook has all the answers you need. Look on the pages listed.

TOP SECRET TIP

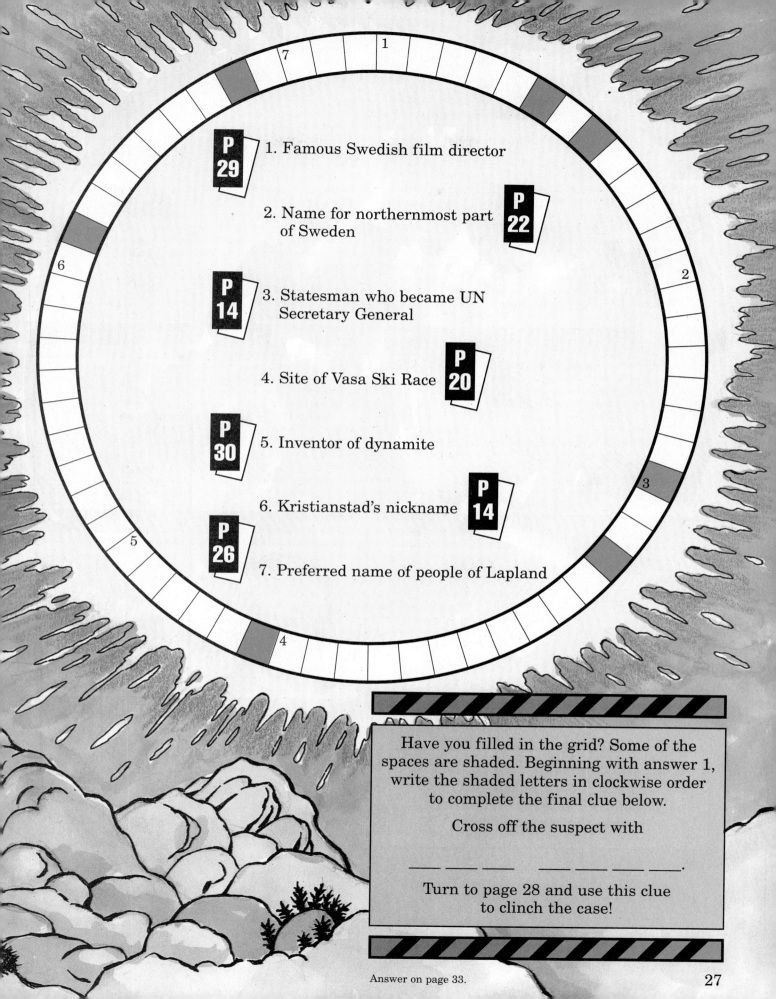

1. Famous Swedish film director   **P 29**

2. Name for northernmost part of Sweden   **P 22**

3. Statesman who became UN Secretary General   **P 14**

4. Site of Vasa Ski Race   **P 20**

5. Inventor of dynamite   **P 30**

6. Kristianstad's nickname   **P 14**

7. Preferred name of people of Lapland   **P 26**

Have you filled in the grid? Some of the spaces are shaded. Beginning with answer 1, write the shaded letters in clockwise order to complete the final clue below.

Cross off the suspect with

_____ _____.

Turn to page 28 and use this clue to clinch the case!

Answer on page 33.

WHO DID IT?

To catch the crook, you must solve the puzzles on pages 2, 10, 14, 20, and 26. Each time you solve a puzzle, you will be able to cross one suspect off the list. When there's only one suspect left, you will have found your thief!

SUSPECT LIST

Björn Toorun

Greta Scapes

Inga Rate

Dylan Pickles

Leif DeKash

Evelyn Tensions

When you cross off a suspect, do it in pencil. If you solve a puzzle incorrectly, you may need to erase in order to find the correct answer.

Have you found the crook? You can check your answer on the answer pages.

FINAL ANSWER:
The crook who did it is

WHAT WAS STOLEN?

To find out what was stolen, you'll need to solve the puzzles that begin on pages 4, 8, 16, and 22. Each puzzle will give you a word or words to write on the lines. When you have completed all the puzzles, you can use those clue words and the instructions below to crack this code.

Pages 4-5: _____

Pages 8-9: _____

Pages 16-17: _____

Pages 22-23: _____ and _____

When you have solved all the puzzles and filled in the lines above, you're ready to begin! First, read the clue word from the puzzle on pages 4-5. Then go to the color-coded letter box. Write each letter from boxes of that color, in order from left to right and top to bottom, in the spaces below. Do this for each of the color clues, going in puzzle order, until you've filled in all the spaces.

LETTER BOX

R	R	T	F	S	H	R	O	O	O	B
E	M	E	W	S	T	Y	N	A	W	L
E	H	E	A	E	N	T	D	P	V	J
E	I	A	A	H	W	S	L	U	E	A
T	L	L	C	H	E	H	S	T	C	E

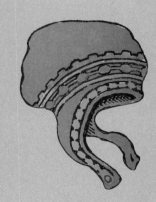

FINAL ANSWER:
The stolen item is

___ ___ ___   ___ ___ ___ ___ ___   ___ ___ ___ ___ ___ ___

___ ___ ___ ___ ___ ___   ___ ___ ___ ___ ___ ___ ___ ___

WHERE IS IT HIDDEN?

To find out where the stolen goods are hidden, you must solve the puzzles on pages 1, 6, 12, 18, and 24. Each puzzle will give you enough information to cross one location off the list below. When you've solved all the puzzles, one place will be left. That is where the stolen loot is hidden.

In the FORMAL GARDENS at Drottningholm Palace

In a WINDMILL on Öland Island

On top of MOUNT KEBNEKAISE

Under a SMÖRGÅSBORD TABLE in Östersund

On AN ISLAND in the Stockholm archipelago

In an old COPPER MINE at Falun

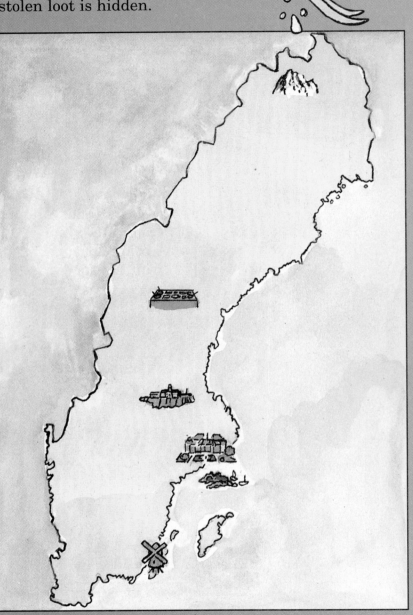

FINAL ANSWER:
It's hidden

TOP SECRET DECODER PAGE

Use the extra space on this page to work out your puzzles.

The next two pages contain the answers for every puzzle and
for the Top Secret Mystery. Do not peek unless you're stuck
on a puzzle and need help.

TOP SECRET ANSWER KEY

PAGE 1: EX-CLUE-SIVE SCREENING

The decoded message says

OUR AGENT ON TOP OF MOUNT KEBNEKAISE FOUND NOTHING BUT BEAUTIFUL VIEWS.

On page 30, cross off Mount Kebnekaise.

PAGES 2-3: HIDDEN CROOKS

Björn Toorun is not in the picture. Cross him off the suspect list on page 28.

PAGES 4-5: WHAT'S ON SAIL?

The message says

SET SAIL WITH A CLUE: THE CODE WORD IS "BLUE."

Write this code word on page 29.

PAGES 6-7: PLAY IT AGAIN

1. $\underset{1}{P}\,A\,\underset{2}{D}\,J\,E\,L\,A\,\underset{3}{N}\,T\,A$

2. $\underset{4}{G}\,Ö\,T\,A\quad \underset{5}{A}\,L\,V$

3. $\underset{6}{H}\,Y\,D\,R\,O\,E\,L\,E\,C\,T\,\underset{7}{R}\,I\,C\,I\,T\,\underset{8}{Y}$

4. $\underset{9}{S}\,K\,Å\,N\,\underset{10}{E}$

5. $L\,\underset{11}{I}\,D\,I\,N\,G\,Ö\,L\,\underset{12}{O}\,P\,P\,E\,T$

6. $S\,\underset{13}{E}\,L\,M\,A\quad L\,\underset{14}{A}\,G\,E\,R\,L\,Ö\,\underset{15}{F}$

7. $\underset{16}{U}\,P\,P\,S\,A\,\underset{17}{L}\,A$

$\underset{6}{H}\,\underset{12}{O}\,\underset{1}{P}\,\underset{10}{E}\quad \underset{8}{Y}\,\underset{12}{O}\,\underset{16}{U}\,\underset{7}{'}\!R\,\underset{10}{E}\quad \underset{3}{N}\,\underset{12}{O}\,\underset{4}{T}\quad \underset{6}{H}\,\underset{16}{U}\,\underset{3}{N}\,\underset{14}{G}\,\underset{7}{R}\,\underset{8}{Y}.$

$\underset{4}{T}\,\underset{6}{H}\,\underset{10}{E}\quad \underset{9}{S}\,\underset{4}{T}\,\underset{12}{O}\,\underset{17}{L}\,\underset{10}{E}\,\underset{3}{N}\quad \underset{11}{I}\,\underset{4}{T}\,\underset{10}{E}\,\underset{13}{M}\quad \underset{11}{I}\,\underset{9}{S}$

$\underset{3}{N}\,\underset{12}{O}\,\underset{4}{T}\quad \underset{3}{N}\,\underset{10}{E}\,\underset{5}{A}\,\underset{7}{R}\quad \underset{15}{F}\,\underset{12}{O}\,\underset{12}{O}\,\underset{2}{D}.$

Cross off the smörgåsbord table from the list on page 30, since it *is* near food.

PAGES 8-9: ROCKING RUNES

Translated into English, the runic message says IT IS "TAN." Write the word *tan* on the correct line on page 29.

PAGES 10-11: FISH STORIES

Lars was the first one up (4:10 a.m.), so he saw the crook—someone whose shirt had *no* stars. Cross off Greta Scapes on page 28. She's the only suspect whose shirt *does* have stars on it.

PAGES 12-13: "SMÖR" CLUES

1. **s** 2. **n** 3. **e** 4. **d** 5. **r** 6. **a** 7. **g**

From last to first, the circled letters spell GARDENS. On page 30, cross off the formal gardens at Drottningholm Palace.

PAGES 14-15: HEAD OF THE GLASS

The message says

CROSS OFF THE SNAKE
WHO EATS ANGEL
FOOD CAKE

Cross off Evelyn Tensions on page 28—angel food cake is her favorite food.